Maths BASICS

FOR AGES 10-11 KEY STAGE 2

Contents

How to use this book

Numeracy Basics helps you to help your child practise many important basic skills covered in the *National Numeracy Strategy* and *National Curriculum*.

Each book is divided into *30 units* of work which focus on *one clear* objective.

Most of the units are designed using the same easy-to-follow *key features*. In some cases these features are combined into one activity, offering further practice where appropriate.

Title
Target learning objective.

Look and learn
Introduces and explains the target objective. Provides an example to illustrate it.

Practice
Provides straightforward practice activities based on the target objective.

Challenge
Provides activities to extend and challenge.

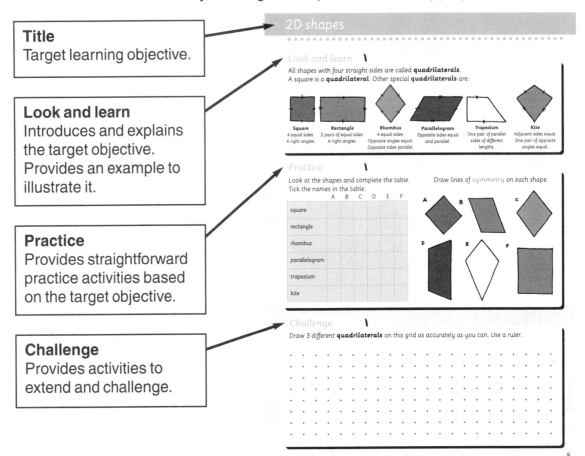

Suggested way of using the book

- It is suggested that your child works systematically through the book.

- Try tackling one unit per week.

- Read through and discuss the *Look and learn* section with your child to make sure the key objective is understood.

- Help your child get started on the Practice section.

- After this, your child can start to work fairly independently through the page, but will need further support and encouragement.

- The answers are supplied at the end of the book for checking each unit on its completion.

Enjoy the book!

Look and learn

To **multiply** by 1000, move all the digits three places to the left.

To **divide** by 1000, move all the digits three places to the right.

		3	6	·	4		
3	6	4	0	0	·		

		4	1	3	0	·			
					4	·	1	3	0

Practice

Multiply each of these by 100.

745 → [ ]   298 → [ ]

5610 → [ ]   3114 → [ ]

8·65 → [ ]   21·8 → [ ]

Divide each of these by 100.

4800 → [ ]   62100 → [ ]

27300 → [ ]   38000 → [ ]

4910 → [ ]   3158 → [ ]

Multiply each of these by 1000.

26 → [ ]   314 → [ ]

968 → [ ]   2317 → [ ]

6·05 → [ ]   19·8 → [ ]

0·003 → [ ]   1·65 → [ ]

Divide each of these by 1000.

294000 → [ ]   817000 → [ ]

6148000 → [ ]   1722000 → [ ]

81500 → [ ]   13100 → [ ]

62 → [ ]   40 → [ ]

Challenge

Write in the missing numbers.

48 x ◯ = 4800   ◯ x 1000 = 570   387 ÷ 100 = ◯

◯ ÷ 100 = 0·06   61·3 x ◯ = 61300   ◯ ÷ 1000 = 8·5

0·07 x ◯ = 7   ◯ ÷ 10 = 16·05   ◯ x 100 = 9413

Division facts

Look and learn

Use the **multiplication** facts to help work out **division** facts.

$$3 \times 8 = 24 \qquad 24 \div 3 = 8 \qquad 24 \div 8 = 3$$

Practice

Write the related **division** facts.

$4 \times 7 = \square$ $8 \times 6 = \square$

$\square \div 4 = 7$ $\square \div 8 = 6$
$\square \div 7 = 4$ $\square \div 6 = 8$

$9 \times 3 = \square$ $7 \times 8 = \square$

$\square \div 3 = 9$ $\square \div 8 = 7$
$\square \div 9 = 3$ $\square \div 7 = 8$

$6 \times 9 = \square$ $5 \times 9 = \square$

$\square \div 6 = 9$ $\square \div 5 = 9$
$\square \div 9 = 6$ $\square \div 9 = 5$

Answer these as **quickly as you can**.
Write the answers on paper.
Try to beat your time.

1. $48 \div 6$ 9. $27 \div 3$ 17. $32 \div 8$
2. $90 \div 10$ 10. $80 \div 8$ 18. $16 \div 4$
3. $54 \div 9$ 11. $32 \div 4$ 19. $72 \div 9$
4. $64 \div 8$ 12. $15 \div 5$ 20. $21 \div 3$
5. $35 \div 5$ 13. $81 \div 9$ 21. $60 \div 10$
6. $36 \div 6$ 14. $45 \div 5$ 22. $30 \div 5$
7. $18 \div 3$ 15. $63 \div 7$ 23. $48 \div 8$
8. $36 \div 4$ 16. $49 \div 7$ 24. $28 \div 4$

Challenge

Write in the **missing numbers** for these multiplication grids.

x	7	8	4
6	42		
9			
		40	

x	6		5
	48		
			35
9		27	

x			
	56	42	21
	40	30	15
	72	54	27

Practice

- What is the cost of a **spade**, a **fork** and some **grass seed**? ⬚

- How much change from **£100** would there be if you bought a **lawnmower**? ⬚

- What is the cost of **two pots** and a **hedge trimmer**? ⬚

- What would be the total cost of five packets of grass seed? ⬚

- What change would there be from **£50**? ⬚

- What is the difference in price between the spade and the fork? ⬚

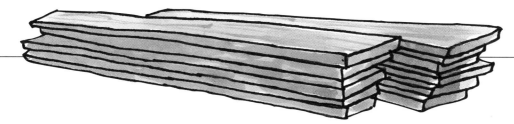

- A piece of wood is 27·68 **metres** long. Five equal lengths are cut from the wood leaving a length of 3·68 **metres**. What is the length of each of the five pieces? ⬚

- Kelly travels 42·84 **kilometres** by car and 1350 **metres** on foot.
  How far does she travel altogether in **kilometres**? ⬚
  How far does she travel altogether in **metres**? ⬚

- A full bucket holds 2·8 **litres**. A jug holds 0·4 **litres**.
  How many jugs will fill the bucket? ⬚

- A bus travels 15·8 **kilometres** in one journey. The bus does this journey six times a day Monday to Friday and four times a day on Saturday and Sunday. How many **kilometres** does the bus travel in total in one week? ⬚

- Eight boxes of cereal cost a total of £12·48.
  What is the cost of one box of cereal? ⬚

5

Fractions

Look and learn

$$\frac{3}{5}$$ → Numerator
→ Denominator

Simplifying fractions:

$$\frac{4}{10} \begin{array}{c} \div 2 \\ \div 2 \end{array} \to \frac{2}{5}$$

$$\frac{3}{6} \begin{array}{c} \div 3 \\ \div 3 \end{array} \to \frac{1}{2}$$

Ordering fractions
To order fractions change them so they all have the same denominator.
↓

$$\frac{1}{2} = \frac{6}{12} \qquad \frac{2}{3} = \frac{8}{12} \qquad \frac{3}{4} = \frac{9}{12}$$

Practice

Complete these equivalent fractions.

$$\frac{1}{4} = \frac{\Box}{8}$$

$$\frac{1}{2} = \frac{8}{\Box}$$

$$\frac{\Box}{5} = \frac{16}{20}$$

$$\frac{9}{10} = \frac{45}{\Box}$$

$$\frac{2}{5} = \frac{6}{\Box}$$

$$\frac{2}{3} = \frac{\Box}{9}$$

$$\frac{3}{\Box} = \frac{30}{100}$$

$$\frac{7}{8} = \frac{\Box}{80}$$

Simplify these fractions.

$$\frac{6}{12} \begin{array}{c} \div \Box \\ \div \Box \end{array} \to \frac{\Box}{\Box}$$

$$\frac{9}{15} \begin{array}{c} \div \Box \\ \div \Box \end{array} \to \frac{\Box}{\Box}$$

$$\frac{8}{12} \to \frac{\Box}{\Box}$$

$$\frac{12}{15} \to \frac{\Box}{\Box}$$

$$\frac{6}{24} \to \frac{\Box}{\Box}$$

$$\frac{5}{15} \begin{array}{c} \div \Box \\ \div \Box \end{array} \to \frac{\Box}{\Box}$$

$$\frac{12}{20} \begin{array}{c} \div \Box \\ \div \Box \end{array} \to \frac{\Box}{\Box}$$

$$\frac{15}{20} \to \frac{\Box}{\Box}$$

$$\frac{9}{21} \to \frac{\Box}{\Box}$$

$$\frac{8}{32} \to \frac{\Box}{\Box}$$

Challenge

Write these fractions in order starting with the **smallest**.

$$\frac{1}{2} \qquad \frac{2}{5} \qquad \frac{7}{10} \qquad \frac{3}{4}$$

smallest   largest

$$\frac{3}{8} \qquad \frac{1}{4} \qquad \frac{1}{2} \qquad \frac{5}{6}$$

smallest   largest

Look and learn

Ratios are used to compare two quantities.

The **proportion** is the fraction of the whole.

> For every five tins of white paint there are three tins of red. The ratio of red to white is 3:5.

> **3 out of 8 tins of paint are red.**
> **The proportion of red paint tins is:**
> $$\frac{3}{8}$$

Practice

Ring the correct **ratios** of yellow paint to green paint.

3:5
2:6
3:4

2:3
2:5
1:4

1:8
1:5
1:4

Which **proportion** of each tile pattern is blue?

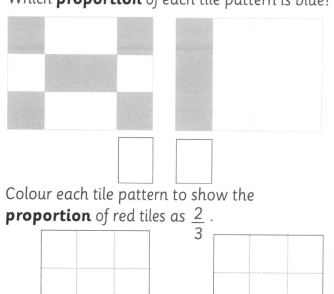

Colour each tile pattern to show the **proportion** of red tiles as $\frac{2}{3}$.

Challenge

Colour these to show the **ratios**.
The ratio of blue to red balls is 1:3.

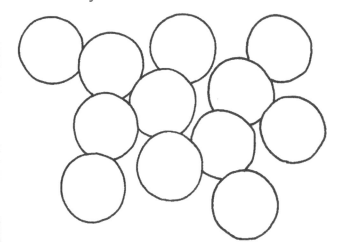

The **ratio** of green to red balls is 3:4.

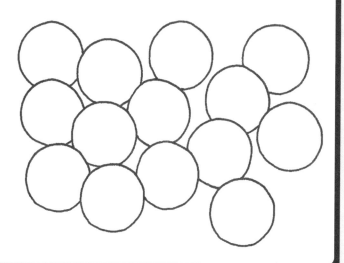

Averages

Look and learn

Mean, mode and median are all different types of average.

Mode: the number that appears most often:

(3) 3 4 7 8

Median: the middle number when listed in order:

3 3 (4) 7 8

Mean: total the value of items and divide this total by the number of items used:

$$\frac{8+7+4+3+3}{5} = \bigcirc{5}$$

Practice

This graph shows the height of ten children.

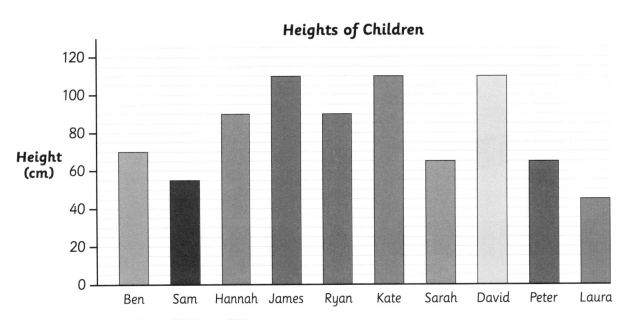

Heights of Children

Height (cm)

Ben Sam Hannah James Ryan Kate Sarah David Peter Laura

Write the heights in order, starting with the tallest child.

What is the height **mode**?

What is the height **median** if Ben's height is discounted?

What is the **mean** height of all the children?

2D shapes

Look and learn

All shapes with four straight sides are called **quadrilaterals**.
A square is a **quadrilateral**. Other special **quadrilaterals** are:

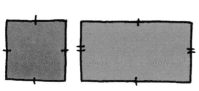 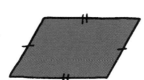 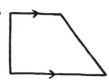 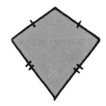

Square	**Rectangle**	**Rhombus**	**Parallelogram**	**Trapezium**	**Kite**
4 equal sides. 4 right angles.	2 pairs of equal sides. 4 right angles.	4 equal sides. Opposite angles equal. Opposite sides parallel.	Opposite sides equal and parallel.	One pair of parallel sides of different lengths.	Adjacent sides equal. One pair of opposite angles equal.

Practice

Look at the shapes and complete the table.
Tick the names in the table.

	A	B	C	D	E	F
square						
rectangle						
rhombus						
parallelogram						
trapezium						
kite						

Draw lines of **symmetry** on each shape.

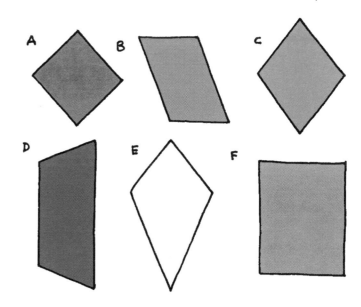

Challenge

Draw 3 different **quadrilaterals** on this grid as accurately as you can. Use a ruler.

Look and learn

Imperial units of capacity include **pints** and **gallons**.

8 pints = 1 gallon

1 gallon ≈ 4·5 litres

1 litre ≈ 1·75 pints

≈ **means approximately equal to**

Practice

Draw conversion graphs for **gallons** to **litres** and **litres** to **pints**.

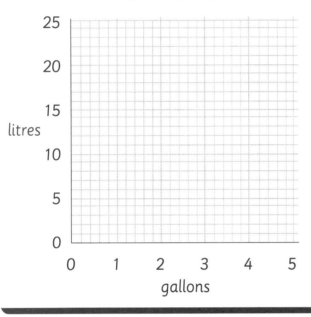

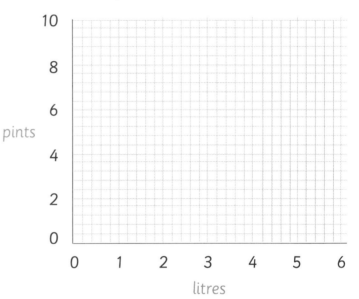

Challenge

Use the graphs to write these missing measures.

0·5 gallons ≈ litres   8 pints ≈ litres   5 litres ≈ pints

 litres ≈ 3 gallons   pints ≈ 3·5 litres

 gallons ≈ 22 litres

Addition and subtraction

Look and learn

Use mental methods to **add** and **subtract**.

450 add 200 is 650, subtract 20 is 630, add 1 is 631.

451 add 100 is 551. 551 add 50 is 601. 601 add 30 is 631.

255 on to 300 is 45. 300 on to 650 is 350. 350 add 45 is 395.

650 minus 250 is 400 Take away another 5 is 395.

$451 + 180$

$650 - 255$

400 add 100 is 500. 51 add 80 is 131. 500 add 131 is 631.

600 take away 200 is 400. 50 subtract 55 is −5. 400 subtract 5 is 395.

Practice

Complete these addition squares.
Add the rows and columns to find the totals.

67	84	
92	45	

108	29	
76	52	

65	155	
175	49	

280	400	
170	220	

450	120	
370	260	

2600	3100	
1700	5800	

Work out the differences between these pairs of numbers.

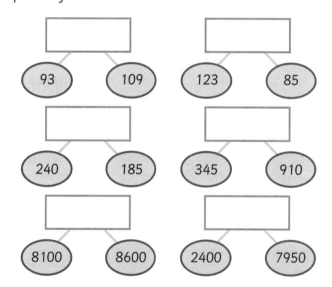

93 109

123 85

240 185

345 910

8100 8600

2400 7950

Challenge

$5 + 6 + 7 = 18$ 5, 6 and 7 are **consecutive** numbers.

Find three **consecutive** numbers to make each of these totals.

☐ + ☐ + ☐ = 57

☐ + ☐ + ☐ = 81

☐ + ☐ + ☐ = 339

☐ + ☐ + ☐ = 504

Look and learn

Looking at the differences between numbers in a **sequence** can show the **pattern** or **rule**.

4 7 10 13 . . .	15 9 3 –3 –9 . . .
The pattern or rule is add 3.	The pattern or rule is subtract 6.

Practice

Continue these **sequences**.
Write the **rule**.

7 11 15 19 __ __ __ __

Rule:

23 15 7 –1 __ __ __ __

Rule:

7·5 9 10·5 12 __ __ __ __

Rule:

Write the missing numbers in these **sequences**.

6		28	39			
0·9	0·89			0·86		
55	40					–35
37					82	91
0·25	0·5				1·5	
		–63	–44	–25		

Challenge

Continue and explain the **sequences**. Do you know what these patterns are called?

1 4 9 16 __ __ __ __

1 3 6 10 __ __ __ __

12

Approximation and rounding

Look and learn

When you round to the nearest 10, 100 or 1000, the half-way postion is important.

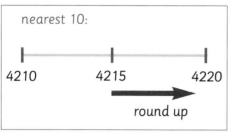

nearest 10:

4210	4215	4220

round up

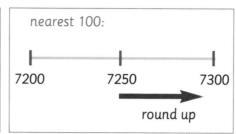

nearest 100:

7200	7250	7300

round up

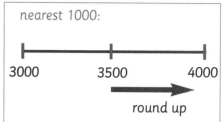

nearest 1000:

3000	3500	4000

round up

Numbers that are half-way or beyond are **rounded up**. The rest are **rounded down**.

Practice

Round these numbers:

	to the nearest 10	to the nearest 100	to the nearest 1000
43179 →			
789155 →			
261004 →			
749968 →			
415584 →			
29465 →			
414563 →			
254564 →			

Challenge

Estimate the numbers which the arrows point to, remembering to round up or down.

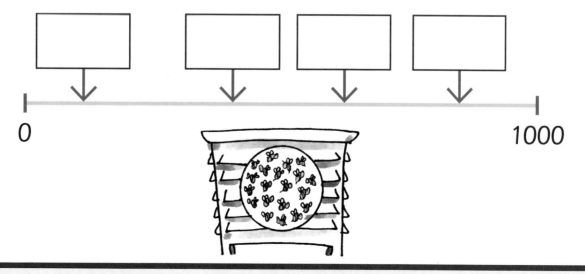

0   1000

Look and learn

8·3 x 7 →

| 8 x 7 = 56 |
| 0·3 x 7 = 2·1 |
| 8·3 x 7 = 58·1 |

8·3 x 7 is **approximately** 8 x 7 which is 56.

Estimate first to check the answer.

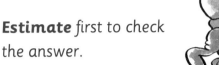

Practice

Circle the correct answer by **approximating**.

6·9 x 4 → 27·6 / 270·6

8·2 x 6 → 4·92 / 49·2

7·8 x 5 → 75 / 39

9·41 x 3 → 28·23 / 282·3

6·07 x 7 → 42·49 / 49·42

Answer these. Remember to **estimate** first.

5·7 x 6 = [ ]   4·9 x 3 = [ ]

1·9 x 8 = [ ]   2·6 x 4 = [ ]

7·2 x 7 = [ ]   3·8 x 6 = [ ]

9·03 x 4 = [ ]   6·14 x 5 = [ ]

5·11 x 9 = [ ]   8·65 x 3 = [ ]

7·28 x 4 = [ ]   0·95 x 8 = [ ]

0·07 x 3 = [ ]   1·63 x 6 = [ ]

Challenge

Use these digits in the calculation below:

 6   4   7   3

[ ] · [ ] [ ]

X [ ]

_____

Arrange them in the calculation to make:

The largest possible answer → [ ]

The smallest possible answer → [ ]

Practice

1·85 kg   **2·63 kg**   **3·94 kg**   **2·09 kg**

- What is the difference in weight between the heaviest and the lightest packages? _____

- What is the total weight of parcels A, B and C? _____

- Which two parcels have a difference in weight of 0·24 kg? _____

- How much heavier is parcel B than parcel A? _____

- What would be the total weight of eight parcel Ds? _____

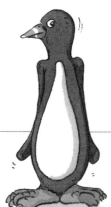

- Which is more: **12 lb** of carrots or **12 kg** of carrots? _____

1 lb = 0.45 kg
1 pt = 0.55 l
1 inch = 2.5 cm
1 mile = 1.6 km

8 litres of water or **8 pints** of water? _____

a **10 cm** line or a **10 inch** line? _____

5 miles or **5 kilometres**? _____

£58·75   £31·40   £28·46   £9·39   £18·63

How much change would you receive from £200, for each shopping list?

2 tennis raquets 1 pair of trainers 1 cricket bat	1 football 3 hockey sticks 1 pair of trainers	1 cricket bat 2 pairs of trainers 1 football
_____	_____	_____

Look and learn

To find $\frac{4}{5}$ of £150:

- Find $\frac{1}{5}$ of 150 → 30

- Then $\frac{4}{5}$ is 30 x 4 → 120

$\frac{4}{5}$ **of £150 is £120**

Practice

What is $\frac{3}{5}$ of:

40 → ☐   15 → ☐

25 → ☐   60 → ☐

5 → ☐   100 → ☐

What is $\frac{7}{10}$ of:

40 → ☐   15 → ☐

25 → ☐   60 → ☐

5 → ☐   100 → ☐

Write these amounts.

$\frac{2}{3}$ of 63cm = ☐ $\frac{1}{5}$ of 750ml = ☐

$\frac{3}{4}$ of 180km = ☐ $\frac{7}{8}$ of 400l = ☐

$\frac{4}{5}$ of 305m = ☐ $\frac{3}{100}$ of 2000m = ☐

$\frac{4}{9}$ of 504g = ☐ $\frac{2}{5}$ of 1050kg = ☐

$\frac{3}{8}$ of 128cm = ☐ $\frac{9}{10}$ of 450g = ☐

Challenge

- What fraction of £8 is 25p?

- What fraction of one year is one week?

- What fraction of one hour is forty-five minutes?

- What fraction of 1 metre is 70cm?

Coordinates

Look and learn

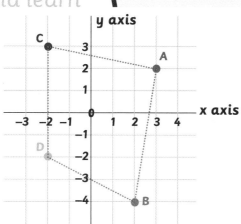

Graphs have **axis**.
Axis are used to plot **coordinates**.

Position A is at (3, 2)

Position B is at (2, −4)

Position C is at (−2, 3)

Position D is at (−2, −2)

Practice

Draw these four **triangles** at the following points:

Triangle A
(2, 2) (4, 6) (7, 3)

Triangle B
(2, −2) (4, −6) (7, −3)

Triangle C
(−2, −2) (−4, −6) (−7, −3)

Triangle D
(−2, 2) (−4, 6) (−7, 3)

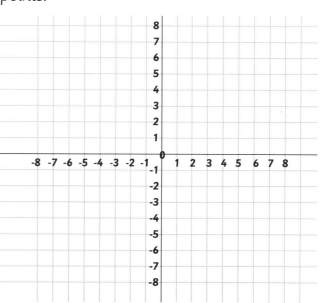

Challenge

Plot the following **coordinates**:

(−4, 1) (−8, 1) (−5, 6) (−1, 6)

Draw a reflection of the shape
and write the coordinates.

mirror line

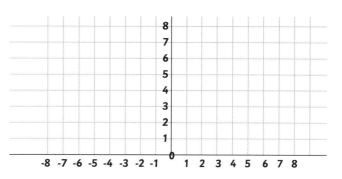

Practice

Some people took part in a sponsored bike ride.
This graph shows the distances cycled.

The distances are grouped in **equal class intervals**. The class interval 6–10 includes 6, 7, 8, 9 and 10 km.

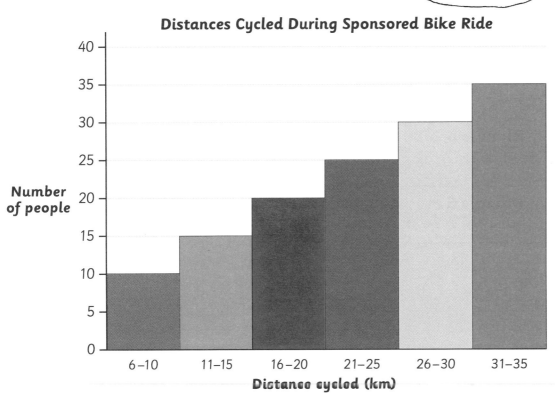

Distances Cycled During Sponsored Bike Ride

• How many people cycled 20 km or less?

• How many people cycled further than 30 km?

• How many more people cycled between 26–30 km than between 11–15 km?

• Which class interval included 20 people?

• Estimate the mean average distance cycled.

• How many people took part altogether in the sponsored bike ride?

Area and perimeter

Look and learn

Area of a rectangle → length x breadth

5cm

3 cm | Area = 5cm x 3cm
= 15 cm²

Perimeter is the distance all the way round.

5cm

3 cm | Perimeter = 5 + 5 + 3 + 3
= 16 cm

Some shapes can be broken into rectangles.

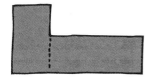 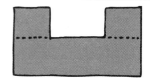 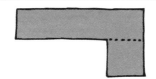

Practice

Calculate the **area** and **perimeter** of each garden plan.

b.

18m

8m

5m

Area = ☐

Perimeter = ☐

5m

Area = ☐

Perimeter = ☐

a.

6m

3m

1m

9m

20m

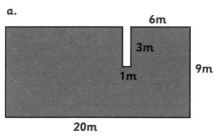

Area = ☐

Perimeter = ☐

c.

3m

9m

5m

7m

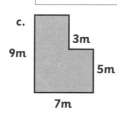

d.

15m

5m

12m

14m

Area = ☐

Perimeter = ☐

3m

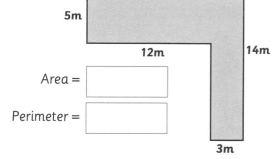

Challenge

Find the **area** of the garden and pond.

- Area of whole garden = ☐

- Area of pond = ☐

- Area of grass = ☐

18 m

8m

6m

10 m

4·5 m

3m

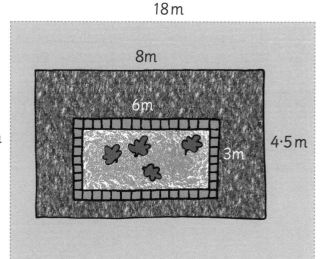

Look and learn

When **adding** and **subtracting** decimals, estimate the answers first and then calculate.

$$4·06 + 3·5 + 4·48 ≈ 12$$

$$9·1 − 3·82 ≈ 5$$

Practice

Write the **approximate** and **actual** answers.

$15·4 + 8·7 =$

Approx:

$18·61 + 9·3 =$

Approx:

$13·67 + 12·28 =$

Approx:

$37·51 + 19·2 =$

Approx:

$25·75 + 31·6 =$

Approx:

$56·85 + 20·98 =$

Approx:

Join the pairs that total 25.

14·52	9.16	6.09	15.84	8.93
18·91	16.07	10.48	10.37	14.63

Challenge

Write pairs of numbers to make these totals.

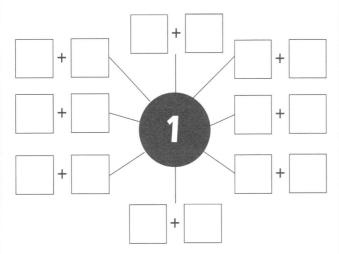

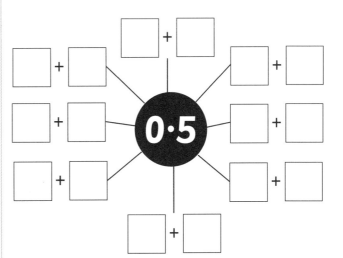

Number problems

Dizzy Dipper £1·90	X-ray Ride £2·05	Super Spin £1·80	Giant £2·15	Mars Mission £1·35	Big Wheel £1·55

Each of these children went on two different rides. Which two rides did they go on?

Alex: £1·50 change from £5:

Harry: £6·30 change from £10:

Rebecca: 15p change from £4:

Emma: £5·95 change from £10:

Which of these rides is the mean average price for the 6 rides:

- 148 children and 14 adults went on a coach trip to the fairground.

  Coaches seat 59 people, so how many coaches were needed?

- In a queue for the Big Wheel, there are three boys for every two girls.

  If 15 boys are in the queue, how many girls are there?

- The Watson family took 1 hour 30 minutes to get to the fairground.

  If they travelled 75 kilometres, what was their average speed? ⬜ km/h

- On the final day of the fair, the prices for the six rides are reduced by 20%.

  What is the new price for each?

Dizzy Dipper	X-ray Ride	Super Spin	Giant	Mars Mission	Big Wheel

Look and learn

Multiples:

> of 2 are 2, 4, 6, 8, 10 . . . and so on.
> of 6 are 6, 12, 18, 24 . . . and so on.
> of 9 are 9, 18, 27, 36 . . . and so on.

Multiples of a number go on and on . . .

Factors are those numbers which will divide exactly into other numbers.

> Factors of 18 → 1, 2, 3, 6, 9, 18
> Factors of 20 → 1, 2, 4, 5, 10, 20

Practice

Write the numbers 1 to 30 on each Venn diagram.

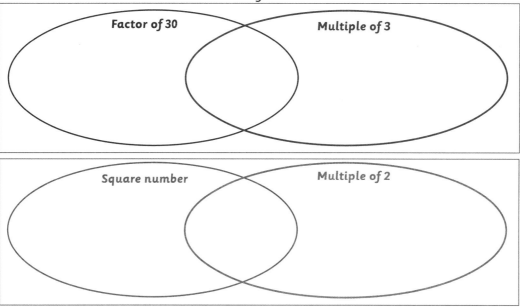

Challenge

Write the numbers 1 to 50 on this Venn diagram.

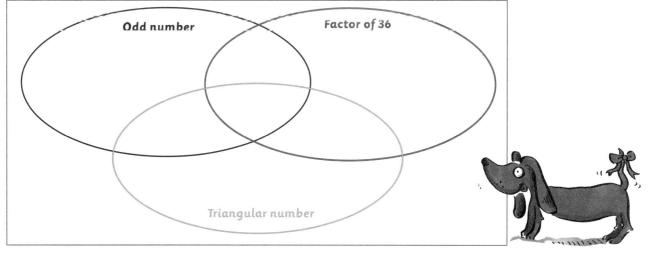

Look and learn

tens	units		tenths	hundredths	thousandths
1	7	•	8	3	5

The decimal point separates units from tenths.

In seventeen point eight three five
the value of the digit three is 3 hundredths or → $\frac{3}{100}$

Practice

Write the value of the circled digit.

87·③84 → ☐

4·00⑥ → ☐

13·4⑤ → ☐

117·⑧05 → ☐

3·0⑥8 → ☐

Continue these patterns for three more numbers.

1·96 →1·97 →1·98

3·018 → 3·019 →

4·947 → 4·948 →

0·998 → 0·999 →

Write approximately which
decimal number these arrows
point to.

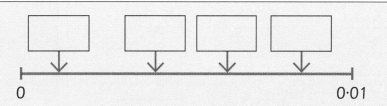

0   0·01

Challenge

Rearrange each of these sets to make a decimal number as near as possible to 1. There must be one number in front of the decimal point, e.g. 6.401.

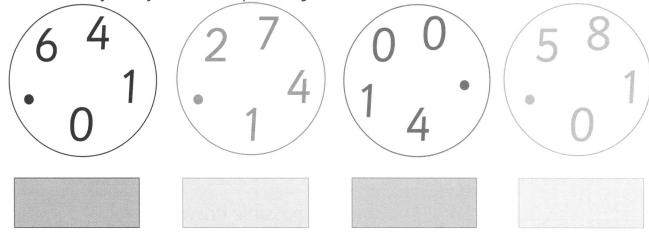

☐   ☐   ☐   ☐

Look and learn

There are different ways to work out multiplication calculations.

$384 \times 27 \rightarrow$

	20	7	
300	6000	2100	→ 8100
80	1600	560	→ 2160
4	80	28	→ +108
			10368

```
   384
 x  27
  7680

  2688
 10368
```

384 x 27 is approximately
400 x 30
↓
12000

Practice

Answer these.

193	261	413
x 24	x 19	x 26

238	419	306
x 31	x 27	x 34

Work out the volume of each cuboid.

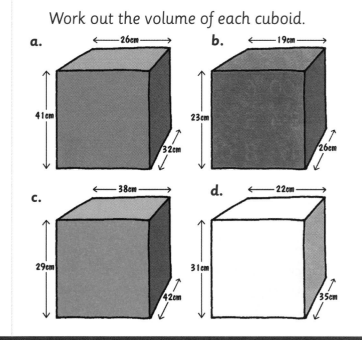

a. 26cm, 41cm, 32cm

b. 19cm, 23cm, 26cm

c. 38cm, 29cm, 42cm

d. 22cm, 31cm, 35cm

Challenge

Choose 4 of these digits to use in the calculation below:

2   4   5   6   8

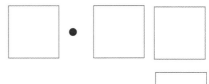

☐ . ☐ ☐

X ☐

Arrange them to make:

The largest possible answer → ☐

The smallest possible answer → ☐

Division

Look and learn

There are different ways to work out division calculations.

$$896 \div 28 \rightarrow$$

$$\begin{array}{r} 32 \\ 28\overline{)896} \\ -840 \quad (\mathbf{30} \times 28) \\ \hline 56 \\ -56 \quad (\mathbf{2} \times 28) \\ \hline \end{array}$$

896 ÷ 28
is approximately
900 ÷ 30
which is 30

Practice

Answer these.

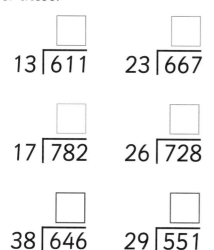

$$13\overline{)611} \quad \square$$
$$23\overline{)667} \quad \square$$
$$17\overline{)782} \quad \square$$
$$26\overline{)728} \quad \square$$
$$38\overline{)646} \quad \square$$
$$29\overline{)551} \quad \square$$

670

952

624

885

714

a. Which of these numbers can be divided exactly by 13?

b. Which of these numbers is exactly divisible by 15?

c. Which of these numbers has a remainder of 4 when divided by 18?

d. Which of these numbers is exactly divisible by 21?

Challenge

Write the missing digits 0–5.

$$\begin{array}{r} 5\,7 \\ 13\overline{)7\,\square\,1} \end{array}$$

$$\begin{array}{r} 3\,2 \\ 26\overline{)8\,\square\,2} \end{array}$$

$$\begin{array}{r} 4\,\square \\ 17\overline{)714} \end{array}$$

It may be useful to write the digits on small pieces of paper and move them around.

$$\begin{array}{r} 3\,1 \\ 26\overline{)8\,\square\,6} \end{array}$$

$$\begin{array}{r} 3\,7 \\ 23\overline{)85\,\square} \end{array}$$

$$\begin{array}{r} 1\,\square \\ 31\overline{)465} \end{array}$$

Decimals

Look and learn

To order **decimals**, write them in a column with the decimal point aligned.

0·81	
0·6	
0·1	
0·02	
0·06	
0·09	

→ Line up decimal points. Write in missing zeros.

0·81
0·10
0·60
0·09
0·02
0·06

Put them in order.

→

0.02
0·06
0·09
0·10
0·60
0·81

Practice

Write these numbers in order, starting with the **smallest**.

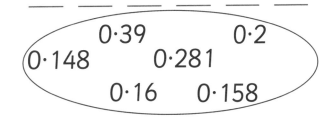

0·7   0·66   0·13   0·4   0·39   0·48

_____ _____ _____ _____ _____ _____

0·148   0·39   0·2   0·281   0·16   0·158

_____ _____ _____ _____ _____ _____

Write the **decimal** number these arrows point to.

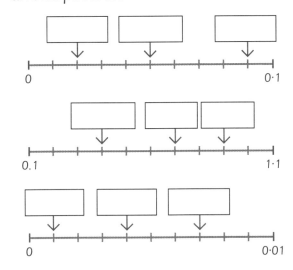

Challenge

Write as many numbers as you can from these four cards, e.g. ·368, 3·86, 86·3.

Percentages

Look and learn

% shows a **fraction** out of 100.

$$35\% = \frac{35}{100}$$
$$= \frac{7}{20}$$

$$60\% = \frac{60}{100}$$
$$= \frac{3}{5}$$

$$10\% \text{ of } £20 \rightarrow \frac{1}{10} \text{ of } £20 = £2$$

$$20\% \text{ of } £20 \rightarrow \text{double } 10\% \rightarrow £4$$

$$1\% \text{ of } £20 \rightarrow \frac{1}{100} \text{ of } £20 = 20p$$

$$2\% \text{ of } £20 \rightarrow \text{double } 1\% \rightarrow 40p$$

Practice

Write as a **%**.

$$\frac{7}{10} = \boxed{}$$
$$\frac{4}{5} = \boxed{}$$
$$\frac{9}{20} = \boxed{}$$
$$\frac{7}{25} = \boxed{}$$
$$\frac{19}{20} = \boxed{}$$

Write as a **fraction**.

$$15\% = \frac{\boxed{}}{20}$$
$$12\% = \frac{\boxed{}}{25}$$
$$8\% = \frac{\boxed{}}{25}$$
$$40\% = \frac{\boxed{}}{5}$$
$$80\% = \frac{\boxed{}}{50}$$

Write as amounts.

20% of 60 cm = ☐ cm

70% of 20 l = ☐ l

5% of 80 kg = ☐ kg

40% of 500 g = ☐ g

12% of 2000 m = ☐ m

55% of 200 cm = ☐ cm

6% of 300 kg = ☐ kg

Challenge

Write the weights of the extra amounts for each pack.

item	weight (g)	pack 1 25% extra (g) new weight:	pack 2 20% extra (g) new weight:
choc bar	80g		
nut crunch	120g		
crisps	32g		
fruit bar	48g		

Practice

This graph shows the number of copies of the videos 'Goals of the Century' and 'Great Sporting Moments' hired out from a shop each month for a year.

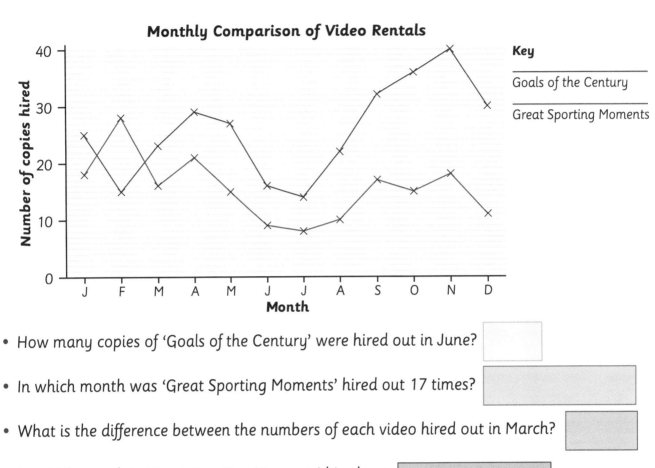

Monthly Comparison of Video Rentals

Key

Goals of the Century

Great Sporting Moments

- How many copies of 'Goals of the Century' were hired out in June?

- In which month was 'Great Sporting Moments' hired out 17 times?

- What is the difference between the numbers of each video hired out in March?

- In which month is 'Great Sporting Moments' hired out more than 'Goals of the Century'?

- How many more copies of 'Goals of the Century' were hired out in November?

- In which month are 12 fewer copies of 'Great Sporting Moments' hired out than 'Goals of the Century'?

- In which month are the fewest number of videos hired?

- What is the total number of each video hired out for the year?

Goal of the Century

Total:

Great Sporting Moments

Total:

Angles

Look and learn

There are some simple rules to remember when working out angles.

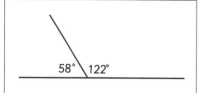

Angles in a straight line equal 180°.

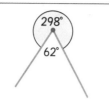

Angles at a point equal 360°.

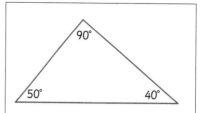

Angles of a triangle add up to 180°.

Practice

Work out the size of the missing angles.

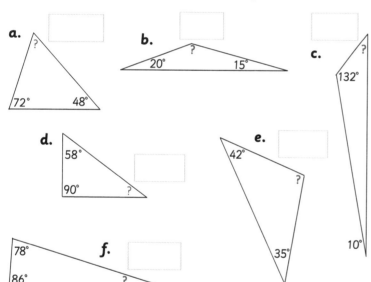

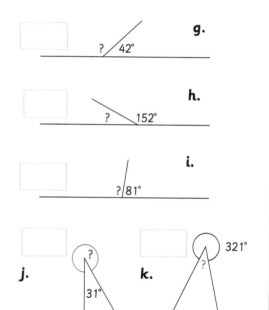

Challenge

Work out the size of the missing angles.

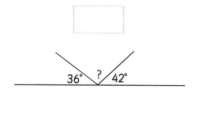

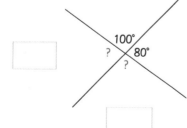

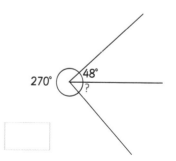

Look and learn

am → **before midday**
(stands for ante meridian)

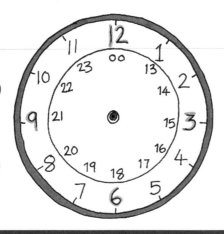

pm → **after midday**
(stands for post meridian)

The 24-hour clock uses four digits:

02 : 35 → 2 : 35am
14 : 35 → 2 : 35pm

Midnight is 00 : 00

Practice

Write these times using the 24-hour clock.

4 : 15pm → ☐   8 : 38pm → ☐

11 : 05pm → ☐   10 : 18pm → ☐

1 : 55pm → ☐   2 : 32pm → ☐

Write these times using **am** and **pm**.

14 : 45 → ☐   10 : 08 → ☐

23 : 25 → ☐   06 : 50 → ☐

11 : 37 → ☐   17 : 18 → ☐

Write these in order from am to pm.

7 : 45am   07:05   13:25
              21:40
    9:30am   10:34pm
11:34pm
        11:04   23:15   5:42pm

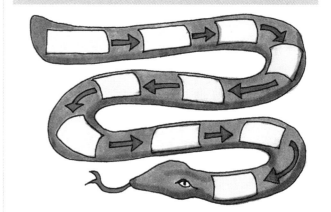

Challenge

These clocks are 35 minutes slow. Write the correct times.

e. ☐

a. ☐

c. ☐

g. ☐

b. ☐

 01·14   d. ☐

   f. ☐

h. ☐

Addition and subtraction

Look and learn

When adding and subtracting **decimal numbers**, make sure the **decimal points** all line up.

17·05 + 6·9 + 381·82

```
    1 7 · 0 5
        6 · 9
  + 3 8 1 · 8 2
  _____

  _____
```

146·69 − 38·4

```
    1 4 6 · 6 9
  −    3 8 · 4
  _____

  _____
```

Practice

Use three numbers from the set given to write different addition calculations.

```
+          +          +
_____     _____     _____

_____     _____     _____


+          +          +
_____     _____     _____

_____     _____     _____
```

16.83
21.07
39.8
42.79
138.6
121.52
97.91
83.5

Use two numbers from the set given to write different subtraction calculations.

```
−          −          −
_____     _____     _____

_____     _____     _____


−          −          −
_____     _____     _____

_____     _____     _____
```

Challenge

Write the missing digits 0–9 in the spaces.

```
  3 ☐ 9 . 6 9        2 7 ☐ . 9          1 0 ☐ . 9          ☐ 6 4 . 8 2
−   5 8 . 7 4      − 1 ☐ 6 . 7 1      −   ☐ 8 . 7        − 2 1 5 . ☐
_____      _____      _____      _____
  2 7 ☐ . 9 ☐        1 3 5 . 1 9          1 8 . 2          2 4 ☐ . 1 2
```

Equations

Look and learn

Equations have symbols or letters instead of numbers.
You need to work out the missing numbers.

$\dfrac{a}{2}$ this means divide a by 2

$\boxed{x} + 4 = 7$

Use subtraction:
7 − 4 is 3,
3 + 4 = 7

$3y = 15$

This means y **multiplied by 3** is 15, so divide 15 by 3 to find y = 5.

$2x + 3 = 9$

Take 3 away from 9 and you are left with 6.
Divide 6 by 2 to find $x = 3$.

Practice

Fill in the missing numbers.

$3 + \boxed{} = 15$

$14 - \boxed{} = 9$

$\boxed{} - 9 = 3$

$3 \times \boxed{} = 21$

$3 \times \boxed{} + 1 = 7$

$(3 \times \boxed{}) - 6 = 18$

Work out the value of each letter

$x + 3 = 9$
$x = \boxed{}$

$4y = 16$
$y = \boxed{}$

$15 - a = 8$
$a = \boxed{}$

$7 + b = 19$
$b = \boxed{}$

$\dfrac{c}{2} = 8$
$c = \boxed{}$

$x + 6 = 15$
$x = \boxed{}$

$4a = 20$
$a = \boxed{}$

$5 + y = 19$
$y = \boxed{}$

$3a = 18$
$a = \boxed{}$

$7c = 21$
$c = \boxed{}$

$x - 8 = 19$
$x = \boxed{}$

$14 - y = 11$
$y = \boxed{}$

Challenge

Work out the value of each letter.

$3x + 5 = 17$

$4y - 3 = 13$

$16 - 2a = 6$

$5c + 3 = 13$